GCSE English AQA Anthology

The Workbook

Poems from Different Cultures

AQA A Specification — Foundation Level

This book is for anyone doing GCSE AQA Anthology at Foundation Level.

It contains lots of tricky questions designed to hone your poetry skills —
because that's the only way you'll get any better.

It's also got some daft bits in to try and make the whole
experience at least vaguely entertaining for you.

What CGP is all about

Our sole aim here at CGP is to produce the highest quality
books — carefully written, immaculately presented and
dangerously close to being funny.

Then we work our socks off to get them out to you
— at the cheapest possible prices.

Edward Kamau Brathwaite

<u>Edward Kamau Brathwaite</u> was born in 1930 in Barbados in the West Indies. He's a poet and historian, and he's interested in links between slave nations and their African origins.

Limbo

And limbo stick is the silence in front of me
limbo

limbo
limbo like me
5 *limbo*
limbo like me

long dark night is the silence in front of me
limbo
limbo like me

10 stick hit sound
and the ship like it ready

stick hit sound
and the dark still steady

limbo
15 *limbo like me*

long dark deck and the water surrounding me
long dark deck and the silence is over me

limbo
limbo like me

20 stick is the whip
and the dark deck is slavery

stick is the whip
and the dark deck is slavery

limbo
25 *limbo like me*

drum stick knock
and the darkness is over me

knees spread wide
and the water is hiding

30 *limbo*
limbo like me

knees spread wide
and the dark ground is under me

down
35 down
down

and the drummer is calling me

limbo
limbo like me

40 sun coming up
and the drummers are praising me

out of the dark
and the dumb gods are raising me

up
45 up
up

and the music is saving me

hot
slow
50 step

on the burning ground.

<u>POEM DICTIONARY</u>
Limbo has several meanings —
1.   The West Indian dance, crouching backwards to pass under a horizontal stick — said to have originated from the experience of moving round in the cramped decks of slave ships
2.   An imaginary place for the unwanted or forgotten
3.   In Christianity, a place where infants who die before baptism go

Limbo

Q1   What does the phrase "knees spread wide" tell you about what it's like on the ship?

....

....

Q2   Give an example of imagery (visual descriptions) in the poem.

....

....

Q3   What effect does the rhythm of lines 10 and 12 have?

....

....

....

Q4   a)   Why do you think the poet repeats the lines _"limbo limbo like me"_?

....

....

....

      b)   Find another example of repetition in the poem and describe the effect it has.

....

....

....

Q5   Pick out a phrase from the poem which stands out to you. Explain why you like or dislike it.

....

....

....

....

Tatamkhulu Afrika

Tatamkhulu Afrika was born in Egypt in 1920 but raised as a white South African in District Six of Cape Town. When apartheid was introduced, he refused to be classed as a "superior" white. He joined the African National Congress (ANC) and was a political prisoner because of his fight against apartheid.

Nothing's Changed

Small round hard stones click
under my heels,
seeding grasses thrust
bearded seeds
5   into trouser cuffs, cans,
trodden on, crunch
in tall, purple-flowering,
amiable weeds.

District Six.
10 No board says it is:
but my feet know,
and my hands,
and the skin about my bones,
and the soft labouring of my lungs,
15 and the hot, white, inwards turning
anger of my eyes.

Brash with glass,
name flaring like a flag,
it squats
20 in the grass and weeds,
incipient Port Jackson trees:
new, up-market, haute cuisine,
guard at the gatepost,
whites only inn.

25 No sign says it is:
but we know where we belong.

I press my nose
to the clear panes, know,
before I see them, there will be
30 crushed ice white glass,
linen falls,
the single rose.

Down the road,
working man's cafe sells
35 bunny chows.
Take it with you, eat
it at a plastic table's top,
wipe your fingers on your jeans,
spit a little on the floor:
40 it's in the bone.

I back from the glass,
boy again,
leaving small mean O
of small, mean mouth.
45 Hands burn
for a stone, a bomb,
to shiver down the glass.
Nothing's changed.

POEM DICTIONARY

amiable — likeable / friendly
incipient — developing, just starting
Port Jackson trees — large pine trees
haute cuisine — high-class, expensive food
bunny chows — cheap food for the poor

Nothing's Changed

Q1   Complete the table below with phrases from the poem which show how the inn and the cafe differ.

	The inn	The cafe
Type of food		
Eating surface		
Hygiene / cleanliness		

Q2   What impression do you get of District Six from the descriptions in the first verse?
What words give you this impression?

....

....

....

Q3   What effect do lines 10 and 25 have?

....

....

....

....

Q4   Why does the poet want to act violently at the end of the poem?

....

....

....

Q5   Now choose a phrase from the poem which stands out to you. Explain why you like or dislike it.

....

....

....

....

Grace Nichols

Grace Nichols was born in Guyana in 1950. She was a journalist in the Caribbean until she moved to Britain in 1977. Both of these cultures and the ways they are connected are important to her.

Island Man

(for a Caribbean island man in London who
still wakes up to the sound of the sea)

Morning
and island man wakes up
to the sound of blue surf
in his head
5   the steady breaking and wombing

wild seabirds
and fishermen pushing out to sea
the sun surfacing defiantly
from the east
10   of his small emerald island
he always comes back   groggily groggily

Comes back to sands
of a grey metallic soar
                 to surge of wheels
15   to dull North Circular roar

muffling muffling
his crumpled pillow waves
island man heaves himself

Another London day

POEM DICTIONARY
North Circular — a busy London road

Island Man

Q1   Find two phrases from the poem — one about the Caribbean and
        one about London — which show how their colours are different.

Caribbean   ....

London   ....

Q2   Which phrase is repeated on different lines to show that the man is gradually returning to reality?

....

Q3   How does the poet create the effect of being in a dream?

....

....

....

Q4   Describe the unusual layout on lines 11 and 14 and suggest why the poet has done this.

....

....

....

....

Q5   How do you think the man feels at the end of the poem? Give a relevant quote.

....

....

....

....

Q6   Now select a phrase from the poem which you can relate to and explain why you chose it.

....

....

....

....

Imtiaz Dharker

Imtiaz Dharker was born in Pakistan in 1954. She has said that she believes identity comes from "beliefs and states of mind", rather than nationality or religion.

Blessing

The skin cracks like a pod.
There never is enough water.

Imagine the drip of it,
the small splash, echo
5   in a tin mug,
the voice of a kindly god.

Sometimes, the sudden rush
of fortune. The municipal pipe bursts,
silver crashes to the ground
10   and the flow has found
a roar of tongues. From the huts,
a congregation: every man woman
child for streets around
butts in, with pots,
15   brass, copper, aluminium,
plastic buckets,
frantic hands,

and naked children
screaming in the liquid sun,
20   their highlights polished to perfection,
flashing light,
as the blessing sings
over their small bones.

POEM DICTIONARY
municipal — to do with the city

Blessing

Q1   Write down three words or phrases in the poem which are linked to religion.

i) ....   ii) ....   iii) ....

Q2   Find a phrase from the poem which suggests:

a) that the villagers are desperate to get at the spilt water.   ....

b) that a miracle has happened.   ....

Q3   How do you know that water is very precious to the people in the poem?
Use a quote from the poem in your answer.

....

....

Q4   What impression do lines 1-6 give us of everyday life for the people in the poem?
Support your answer with a relevant quote.

....

....

....

....

Q5   What is the effect of the descriptions of the items the people use to collect the water?

....

....

....

....

Q6   Now you're familiar with the poem, choose a phrase which stands out to you.
Then explain why you like or dislike it.

....

....

....

....

Lawrence Ferlinghetti

Lawrence Ferlinghetti was born in New York in 1919. He settled in San Francisco and is interested in how different cultures and races mix. He's concerned about the growing gap between rich and poor.

Two Scavengers in a Truck,
Two Beautiful People in a Mercedes

At the stoplight waiting for the light
                     nine a.m. downtown San Francisco
a bright yellow garbage truck
           with two garbagemen in red plastic blazers
5   standing on the back stoop
                one on each side hanging on
and looking down into
                an elegant open Mercedes
with an elegant couple in it
10 The man
       in a hip three-piece linen suit
          with shoulder-length blond hair & sunglasses
The young blond woman so casually coifed
           with a short skirt and colored stockings
15   on the way to his architect's office

And the two scavengers up since four a.m.
                 grungy from their route
       on the way home
The older of the two with grey iron hair
20   and hunched back
      looking down like some
        gargoyle Quasimodo
And the younger of the two
         also with sunglasses & long hair
25   about the same age as the Mercedes driver

And both scavengers gazing down
             as from a great distance
    at the cool couple
    as if they were watching some odorless TV ad
30   in which everything is always possible

And the very red light for an instant
        holding all four close together
    as if anything at all were possible
             between them
35   across that small gulf
      in the high seas
          of this democracy

POEM DICTIONARY
stoop — rear footplate of a truck
coifed — stylishly arranged hair
Quasimodo — the fictional hunchbacked bell ringer of Notre Dame

hip — fashionable
gargoyle — a carved monster on a church wall
odorless — with no smell (American spelling)

Two Scavengers in a Truck, Two Beautiful People in a Mercedes

Q1   There are loads of contrasts in this poem. Fill in the table below using words from the poem to show how different from each other the scavengers and the beautiful people are.

	The Scavengers	The Beautiful People
Their job		
Their transport		
Their hair		
Their clothes		

Q2   Write down three words in the poem which make you think of American culture and language.

i) ....   ii) ....   iii) ....

Q3   Why do you think the poet has chosen not to use any full stops?

....

....

Q4   Who does the poet have more sympathy for — the garbagemen or the couple in the Mercedes? Support your answer with a quote.

....

....

....

....

Q5   OK, like you've done before, pick out a phrase from the poem and explain why you like or dislike it.

....

....

....

....

Nissim Ezekiel

<u>Nissim Ezekiel</u> was born in Bombay in 1924, to Jewish parents. But he was raised in a mainly Hindu culture, and has been influenced by atheist views.

Night of the Scorpion

I remember the night my mother
was stung by a scorpion. Ten hours
of steady rain had driven him
to crawl beneath a sack of rice.

5 Parting with his poison — flash
of diabolic tail in the dark room —
he risked the rain again.
The peasants came like swarms of flies
and buzzed the name of God a hundred times

10 to paralyse the Evil One.
With candles and with lanterns
throwing giant scorpion shadows
on the mud-baked walls
they searched for him: he was not found.

15 They clicked their tongues.
With every movement that the scorpion made
his poison moved in Mother's blood, they said.
May he sit still, they said.
May the sins of your previous birth

20 be burned away tonight, they said.
May your suffering decrease
the misfortunes of your next birth, they said.
May the sum of evil
balanced in this unreal world

25 against the sum of good
become diminished by your pain.
May the poison purify your flesh
of desire, and your spirit of ambition,
they said, and they sat around

30 on the floor with my mother in the centre,
the peace of understanding on each face.
More candles, more lanterns, more neighbours,
more insects, and the endless rain.
My mother twisted through and through,

35 groaning on a mat.
My father, sceptic, rationalist,
trying every curse and blessing,
powder, mixture, herb and hybrid.
He even poured a little paraffin

40 upon the bitten toe and put a match to it.
I watched the flame feeding on my mother.
I watched the holy man perform his rites
to tame the poison with an incantation.
After twenty hours

45 it lost its sting.

My mother only said
Thank God the scorpion picked on me
and spared my children.

POEM DICTIONARY
diabolic — to do with the devil
diminished — reduced
sceptic — a doubtful person
rationalist — a person who uses
logical thinking to explain things
hybrid — a mixture of things
rites — actions in a ceremony
incantation — religious chanting

© Nissim Ezekiel 'Night of the Scorpion'
from *Poverty Poems*, reproduced by
permission of Oxford University Press
India, New Delhi

Night of the Scorpion

Q1   Write down a phrase from the poem which shows that:

a)   the poet's mother is in pain.

....

b)   the villagers associate the scorpion with the devil.

....

Q2   Pick out one idea from the Hindu religion which is mentioned in the poem.

....

....

Q3   Why do you think the author has chosen to write the poem from the point of view of a child?

....

....

Q4   The poet describes his father as a "sceptic" (line 36). Why is this important?

....

....

....

Q5   What do you think is the poet's attitude towards the neighbours' religious response?
Support your answer with a quote.

....

....

....

....

Q6   Read through the poem again and write down the phrase that stands out the most to you.
Explain why you like or dislike the phrase.

....

....

....

....

Chinua Achebe

Chinua Achebe was born in Nigeria in 1930. He worked for the Nigerian Broadcasting Corporation, but when war broke out in 1967, he joined the government of Biafra (an area that violently split from the rest of Nigeria). He's written lots of poems about war and its effects.

Vultures

In the greyness
and drizzle of one despondent
dawn unstirred by harbingers
of sunbreak a vulture
5   perching high on broken
bone of a dead tree
nestled close to his
mate his smooth
bashed-in head, a pebble
10 on a stem rooted in
a dump of gross
feathers, inclined affectionately
to hers. Yesterday they picked
the eyes of a swollen
15 corpse in a water-logged
trench and ate the
things in its bowel. Full
gorged they chose their roost
keeping the hollowed remnant
20 in easy range of cold
telescopic eyes ...
        Strange
indeed how love in other
ways so particular
25 will pick a corner
in that charnel-house
tidy it and coil up there, perhaps
even fall asleep – her face
turned to the wall!

30 ... Thus the Commandant at Belsen
Camp going home for
the day with fumes of
human roast clinging
rebelliously to his hairy
35 nostrils will stop
at the wayside sweet-shop
and pick up a chocolate
for his tender offspring
waiting at home for Daddy's
40 return...
        Praise bounteous
providence if you will
that grants even an ogre
a tiny glow-worm
45 tenderness encapsulated
in icy caverns of a cruel
heart or else despair
for in the very germ
of that kindred love is
50 lodged the perpetuity
of evil.

POEM DICTIONARY
harbinger — a messenger / a sign of things to come
charnel-house — a place where corpses are stored
Commandant — a commanding officer
Belsen — a Nazi concentration camp
bounteous providence — the good things that God has given to mankind
encapsulated — enclosed
perpetuity — lasting forever

Vultures

Q1   Fill in the table below with phrases from the poem that describe
the different qualities of the vultures and the Commandant.

	The vultures	The Commandant
Ugliness		
Evil		
Kindness		

Q2   What is the purpose of the phrase "if you will" (line 42)?

....

....

Q3   Explain how the poet creates a solemn mood in the poem. Use quotes from the poem in your answer.

....

....

....

....

Q4   What connections does the poet see between the vultures and the Commandant?

....

....

....

....

Q5   No surprise here — pick out a phrase from the poem which stands out to you.
Explain why you like or dislike it.

....

....

....

....

<u>Denise Levertov</u>

<u>Denise Levertov</u> (1923-97) was born in England but moved to New York in 1947. She later became an American citizen, but was strongly opposed to the USA's involvement in the Vietnam War.

What Were They Like?

1) Did the people of Viet Nam
   use lanterns of stone?
2) Did they hold ceremonies
   to reverence the opening of buds?
3) Were they inclined to quiet laughter?
4) Did they use bone and ivory,
   jade and silver, for ornament?
5) Had they an epic poem?
6) Did they distinguish between speech and singing?

1) Sir, their light hearts turned to stone.
   It is not remembered whether in gardens
   stone lanterns illumined pleasant ways.
2) Perhaps they gathered once to delight in blossom,
   but after the children were killed
   there were no more buds)
3) Sir, laughter is bitter to the burned mouth.
4) A dream ago, perhaps. Ornament is for joy.
   All the bones were charred.
5) It is not remembered. Remember,
   most were peasants; their life
   was in rice and bamboo.
   When peaceful clouds were reflected in the paddies
   and the water buffalo stepped surely along terraces,
   maybe fathers told their sons old tales.
   When bombs smashed those mirrors
   there was time only to scream.
6) There is an echo yet
   of their speech which was like a song.
   It was reported that their singing resembled
   the flight of moths in moonlight.
   Who can say? It is silent now.

<u>POEM DICTIONARY</u>
reverence — deep respect or worship
jade — a gemstone, normally green
illumined — lit up
charred — blackened by fire
paddies — waterlogged fields for growing rice
terraces — different levels of fields for farming

What Were They Like?

Q1   What layout style does this poem take? Suggest a reason why the author chose this style.

....

....

....

....

Q2   Find a word which has different meanings in different
parts of the poem and explain how its meaning changes.

....

....

....

Q3   How is the Vietnamese language described?
Use a quote from the poem to back up you answer.

....

....

....

Q4   What impression does the poem give us of the Vietnamese way of life before the war?
Explain your answer with a relevant quote.

....

....

....

Q5   It's time for you to pick out a phrase. Don't forget to explain how it makes you feel.

....

....

....

....

Sujata Bhatt

<u>Sujata Bhatt</u> was born in India in 1956, later lived in the USA and now lives in Germany with her husband. She writes in both English and Gujarati, her mother tongue.

from **Search For My Tongue**

You ask me what I mean
by saying I have lost my tongue.
I ask you, what would you do
if you had two tongues in your mouth,
5   and lost the first one, the mother tongue,
and could not really know the other,
the foreign tongue.
You could not use them both together
even if you thought that way.
10 And if you lived in a place you had to
speak a foreign tongue,
your mother tongue would rot,
rot and die in your mouth
until you had to spit it out.
15 I thought I spit it out
but overnight while I dream,

મને હતું કે આખ્ખી જીભ આખ્ખી ભાષા,
(munay hutoo kay aakhee jeebh aakhee bhasha)
મેં થૂં કી નાખી છે.
20 (may thoonky nakhi chay)
પરં તુ રાત્રે સ્પ્નામાં મારી ભાષા પાછી આવે છે.
(parantoo rattray svupnama mari bhasha pachi aavay chay)
ફૂલની જેમ મારી ભાષા મારી જીભ
(foolnee jaim mari bhasha mari jeebh)
25 મોઢામાં ખીલે છે.
(modhama kheelay chay)
ફૂલની જેમ મારી ભાષા મારી જીભ
(fullnee jaim mari bhasha mari jeebh)
મોઢામાં પાકે છે.
30 (modhama pakay chay)
it grows back, a stump of a shoot
grows longer, grows moist, grows strong veins,
it ties the other tongue in knots,
the bud opens, the bud opens in my mouth,
35 it pushes the other tongue aside.
Everytime I think I've forgotten,
I think I've lost the mother tongue,
it blossoms out of my mouth.

<u>POEM DICTIONARY</u>
mother tongue — a person's first language

Search For My Tongue

Q1   What effect do the Gujarati words have on the visual appearance of the poem?

....

....

Q2   a)   What metaphor does the poet use to represent her mother tongue?

....

....

     b)   What effect do you think the poet is trying to create by using this metaphor?

....

....

....

Q3   Why do you think the poet uses the words "you" and "I" a lot?

....

....

....

Q4   In lines 17-30, we "hear" the Gujarati language. How important do you think this is to the impact of the poem? Explain your answer.

....

....

....

Q5   Now choose a phrase from the poem which appeals to you and explain why you like or dislike it.

....

....

....

....

Tom Leonard

Tom Leonard was born in Glasgow in 1944. He's often written about people's attitudes to different accents, and says he writes in Scottish dialect so that his 'voice' can be heard through his poetry.

from Unrelated Incidents

this is thi
six a clock
news thi
man said n
5   thi reason
a talk wia
BBC accent
iz coz yi
widny wahnt
10 mi ti talk
aboot thi
trooth wia
voice lik
wanna yoo
15 scruff. if
a toktaboot
thi trooth
lik wanna yoo
scruff yi
20 widny thingk
it wuz troo.
jist wanna yoo
scruff tokn.
thirza right
25 way ti spell
ana right way
ti tok it. this
is me tokn yir
right way a
30 spellin. this
is ma trooth
yooz doant no
thi trooth
yirsellz cawz
35 yi canny talk
right. this is
the six a clock
nyooz. belt up.

Unrelated Incidents

Q1   Which repeated phrase suggests the newsreader looks down on working-class people?

....

Q2   Re-write these phrases from the poem into standard English.

a)   "yi widny thingk it wuz troo"

....

b)   "thirza right way ti spell ana right way ti tok it"

....

c)   "yooz doant no thi trooth yirsellz"

....

Q3   What is meant by the phrase "BBC accent"?

....

Q4   Why does the newsreader think that the news shouldn't be read in a regional accent? Support your answer with a quote.

....

....

....

Q5   Why do you think the poet has chosen to put the newsreader's words into Scottish dialect?

....

....

....

Q6   Choose a phrase from the poem that you find interesting. Explain why you chose it.

....

....

....

....

John Agard

John Agard was born in Guyana in South America in 1949, to parents of mixed nationality. He came to Britain in 1977. He likes to perform his poems, and believes humour is an effective way of challenging people's opinions.

Half-Caste

Excuse me
standing on one leg
I'm half-caste

Explain yuself
5   wha yu mean
when yu say half-caste
yu mean when picasso
mix red an green
is a half-caste canvas/
10   explain yuself
wha yu mean
when yu say half-caste
yu mean when light an shadow
mix in de sky
15   is a half-caste weather/
well in dat case
england weather
nearly always half-caste
in fact some o dem cloud
20   half-caste till dem overcast
so spiteful dem dont want de sun pass
ah rass/
explain yuself
wha yu mean
25   when yu say half-caste
yu mean tchaikovsky
sit down at dah piano
an mix a black key
wid a white key
30   is a half-caste symphony/

Explain yuself
wha yu mean
Ah listening to yu wid de keen
half of mih ear
35   Ah lookin at yu wid de keen
half of mih eye
and when I'm introduced to yu
I'm sure you'll understand
why I offer yu half-a-hand
40   an when I sleep at night
I close half-a-eye
consequently when I dream
I dream half-a-dream
an when moon begin to glow
45   I half-caste human being
cast half-a-shadow
but yu must come back tomorrow
wid de whole of yu eye
an de whole of yu ear
50   an de whole of yu mind

an I will tell yu
de other half
of my story

POEM DICTIONARY
Picasso — the name of a 20th Century Spanish painter
Tchaikovsky — the name of a 19th Century Russian classical music composer

Half-Caste

Q1   Give two examples of imagery used in the poem.

   i)   ....

   ii) ....

Q2   How does the poet use humour to get his point across? Support your answer with a quote.

   ....

   ....

   ....

   ....

Q3   How does the poet create an argumentative tone? Include quotes in your answer.

   ....

   ....

   ....

   ....

Q4   At the end of the poem (lines 47-53) what does the poet say people must do before he will tell them "de other half" of his story? Explain what he means in your own words.

   ....

   ....

   ....

   ....

Q5   Which phrase in the poem stands out to you the most? Explain why you like or dislike it.

   ....

   ....

   ....

   ....

Derek Walcott

<u>Derek Walcott</u> was born in St Lucia, in the West Indies, in 1930. His father was English and his mother was African. As well as poetry, he's written plays, and is a painter.

Love After Love

The time will come
When, with elation,
You will greet yourself arriving
At your own door, in your own mirror,
5   And each will smile at the other's welcome,

And say sit here. Eat.
You will love again the stranger who was your self.
Give wine. Give bread. Give back your heart
To itself, to the stranger who has loved you

10 All your life, whom you ignored
For another, who knows you by heart.
Take down the love-letters from the bookshelf

The photographs, the desperate notes,
Peel your own images from the mirror.
15 Sit. Feast on your life.

Love After Love

Q1   Give two examples of religious / ceremonial language in the poem.

   i)   ....

   ii) ....

Q2   Who is the "stranger" that the poet talks about?

   ....

   ....

Q3   What does the poet tell the reader to celebrate? Use a quote from the poem in your answer.

   ....

   ....

   ....

Q4   Why does the poet advise the reader to take down their love-letters and photographs?

   ....

   ....

   ....

Q5   Does the poet think being single is a good or bad thing? Support your answer with a quote.

   ....

   ....

   ....

   ....

Q6   Now choose a phrase from the poem that stands out to you. Explain why you like or dislike it.

   ....

   ....

   ....

   ....

Imtiaz Dharker

Imtiaz Dharker was born in Pakistan in 1954. She has said that she believes identity comes from "beliefs and states of mind", rather than nationality or religion.

This Room

This room is breaking out
of itself, cracking through
its own walls
in search of space, light,
5   empty air.

The bed is lifting out of
its nightmares.
From dark corners, chairs
are rising up to crash through clouds.

10   This is the time and place
to be alive:
when the daily furniture of our lives
stirs, when the improbable arrives.
Pots and pans bang together
15   in celebration, clang
past the crowd of garlic, onions, spices,
fly by the ceiling fan.
No one is looking for the door.

In all this excitement
20   I'm wondering where
I've left my feet, and why

my hands are outside, clapping.

POEM DICTIONARY
improbable — unlikely, incredible

This Room

Q1   Write down three examples of onomatopoeia from the poem.

i)   ....

ii)   ....

iii) ....

Onomatopoeia is when words sound like the thing they're describing e.g "crunch".

Q2   Make a list of objects that are personified (given human qualities) in this poem.

....

....

....

Q3   What do you think "the daily furniture of our lives" means?

....

....

....

Q4   How do you think the poet feels about what is happening? Support your answer with a quote.

....

....

....

....

Q5   Choose a phrase from the poem that interests you — explain why you chose it.

....

....

....

....

Moniza Alvi

Moniza Alvi was born in Pakistan in 1954, to a Pakistani father and an English mother.
She moved to England as a child, and revisited Pakistan for the first time in 1993.

Presents from my Aunts in Pakistan

They sent me a salwar kameez
        peacock-blue,
              and another
   glistening like an orange split open,
5 embossed slippers, gold and black
          points curling.
   Candy-striped glass bangles
        snapped, drew blood.
   Like at school, fashions changed
10   in Pakistan –
the salwar bottoms were broad and stiff,
       then narrow.
My aunts chose an apple-green sari,
   silver-bordered
15   for my teens.

I tried each satin-silken top –
    was alien in the sitting-room.
I could never be as lovely
        as those clothes –
20   I longed
for denim and corduroy.
   My costume clung to me
       and I was aflame,
I couldn't rise up out of its fire,
25   half-English,
       unlike Aunt Jamila.

I wanted my parents' camel-skin lamp –
   switching it on in my bedroom,
to consider the cruelty
30   and the transformation
from camel to shade,
    marvel at the colours
      like stained glass.

My mother cherished her jewellery –
35   Indian gold, dangling, filligree.
      But it was stolen from our car.
The presents were radiant in my wardrobe.
   My aunts requested cardigans
      from Marks and Spencers.

40 My salwar kameez
     didn't impress the schoolfriend
who sat on my bed, asked to see
    my weekend clothes.
But often I admired the mirror-work,
45   tried to glimpse myself
       in the miniature
glass circles, recall the story
   how the three of us
       sailed to England.
50 Prickly heat had me screaming on the way.
   I ended up in a cot
in my English grandmother's dining-room,
   found myself alone,
       playing with a tin boat.

55 I pictured my birthplace
    from fifties' photographs.
       When I was older
there was conflict, a fractured land
    throbbing through newsprint.
60 Sometimes I saw Lahore –
      my aunts in shaded rooms,
screened from male visitors,
   sorting presents,
      wrapping them in tissue.

65 Or there were beggars, sweeper-girls
    and I was there –
      of no fixed nationality,
staring through fretwork
    at the Shalimar Gardens.

POEM DICTIONARY
salwar kameez — Pakistani items of clothing
Lahore — a city in Pakistan
Shalimar Gardens — peaceful, walled gardens in Lahore
filligree — delicate gold jewellery
fretwork — metal bars for decoration

Presents from my Aunts in Pakistan

Q1 Write down three words in the poem which suggest a negative image of Pakistan.

i) .... ii) .... iii) ....

Q2 Explain what you think the following phrases mean:

a) "was alien in the sitting-room"

....

....

....

b) "I admired the mirror-work, tried to glimpse myself in the minature glass circles"

....

....

....

Q3 How clear are the poet's memories of Pakistan? Explain your answer.

....

....

....

Q4 How does the poet feel about her identity at the end of the poem? Support your answer with a quote.

....

....

....

....

Q5 Write down a phrase from the poem that grabs your attention.
Briefly explain why you like or dislike it.

....

....

....

....

Niyi Osundare

Niyi Osundare was born in Nigeria in 1947, and is a Professor of English.
He has often spoken out against military regimes in his home country.

Not my Business

They picked Akanni up one morning
Beat him soft like clay
And stuffed him down the belly
Of a waiting jeep.
5   What business of mine is it
        So long they don't take the yam
        From my savouring mouth?

They came one night
Booted the whole house awake
10 And dragged Danladi out,
Then off to a lengthy absence.
        What business of mine is it
        So long they don't take the yam
        From my savouring mouth?

15 Chinwe went to work one day
Only to find her job was gone:
No query, no warning, no probe –
Just one neat sack for a stainless record.
        What business of mine is it
20   So long they don't take the yam
        From my savouring mouth?

And then one evening
As I sat down to eat my yam
A knock on the door froze my hungry hand.
25 The jeep was waiting on my bewildered lawn
Waiting, waiting in its usual silence.

<u>POEM DICTIONARY</u>
yam — vegetable eaten in hot countries

<u>Not my Business</u>

Q1   What poetic device does the author use to describe the jeep and the lawn?

....

Q2   Why is the title of the poem ironic?

> Irony is when the writer says one thing but means something else. It's a way of being sarcastic or funny.

....

....

....

Q3   Why do you think the poet:

a)   mentions the time of day in the first line of each verse?

....

....

b)   describes the victims by their first names?

....

....

Q4   What effect do the three lines that are repeated have?

....

....

....

....

Q5   Look over the poem again and pick out the phrase that stands out to you most. Explain what effect it has on you.

....

....

....

....

Grace Nichols

Grace Nichols was born in Guyana in 1950. She now lives and writes in Sussex.

Hurricane Hits England

It took a hurricane, to bring her closer
To the landscape.
Half the night she lay awake,
The howling ship of the wind,
5   Its gathering rage,
Like some dark ancestral spectre.
Fearful and reassuring.

Talk to me Huracan
Talk to me Oya
10 Talk to me Shango
And Hattie,
My sweeping, back-home cousin.

Tell me why you visit
An English coast?
15 What is the meaning
Of old tongues
Reaping havoc
In new places?

The blinding illumination,
20 Even as you short-
Circuit us
Into further darkness?

What is the meaning of trees
Falling heavy as whales
25 Their crusted roots
Their cratered graves?

O why is my heart unchained?

Tropical Oya of the Weather,
I am aligning myself to you,
30 I am following the movement of your winds,
I am riding the mystery of your storm.

Ah, sweet mystery,
Come to break the frozen lake in me,
Shaking the foundations of the very trees within me,
35 Come to let me know
That the earth is the earth is the earth.

POEM DICTIONARY
ancestral spectre —
a ghost of the past
Huracan, Oya, Shango —
African storm gods

Hurricane Hits England

Q1   In your own words, write a summary of what happens in the poem.

....

....

....

....

Q2   What real-life event is the poem based on?

....

Q3   What are Huracan, Oya and Shango?

....

....

Q4   How has the character in the poem been feeling before the storm? Use a quotation in your answer.

....

....

....

....

Q5   What do you think the last line of the poem means?

....

....

....

Q6   For one last time — choose a phrase that stands out to you in the poem and explain why you like or dislike it.

....

....

....

....

Identity

These Poems are about Identity:

Limbo (pages 2-3)
Nothing's Changed (pages 4-5)
Island Man (pages 6-7)
Search For My Tongue (pages 18-19)
Unrelated Incidents (pages 20-21)

Half-Caste (pages 22-23)
Love After Love (pages 24-25)
This Room (pages 26-27)
Presents from my Aunts in Pakistan (pages 28-29)
Hurricane Hits England (pages 32-33)

Q1 Write a couple of sentences about your identity.

....

....

....

....

Q2 Choose a poem that you know from the top of the page.
What does this poem say about what people think about themselves?

....

....

....

....

....

EXAM-STYLE QUESTION **Q3** Our identity comes from different parts of our culture. Compare and contrast how the poets examine the idea of identity in 'Search For My Tongue' and one other poem.

Compare:

- the language devices used

- the feelings and attitudes in the poems

- your opinion of each poem.

EXAM-STYLE QUESTION **Q4** Compare the ways the poets deal with identity in 'Limbo' and one other poem.

Compare:

- how the past is used

- the use of poetic devices

- the feelings expressed

- your opinion of each poem.

Politics

These Poems are about Politics:

Nothing's Changed (pages 4-5)
Two Scavengers in a Truck... (pages 10-11)
Vultures (pages 14-15)

What Were They Like? (pages 16-17)
Unrelated Incidents (pages 20-21)
Not my Business (pages 30-31)

Q1   If you were to write a poem about a political issue, which issue would you choose, and why?

....

....

....

....

Q2   Choose a poem from the top of the page that you know well.
       What political situation does the poet describe, and what is his / her attitude towards it?

....

....

....

....

....

EXAM-STYLE QUESTION

Q3   Compare the political ideas presented in 'Two Scavengers in a Truck,
      Two Beautiful People in a Mercedes' and one other poem.

      Compare:

      •   how they address divisions in society

      •   the language and layout used

      •   the attitudes expressed.

EXAM-STYLE QUESTION

Q4   Compare the ways that the poets show how political systems can treat people
      unfairly in 'Not my Business' and one other poem.

      Compare:

      •   the inequality described

      •   the language used to describe them

      •   the feelings and attitudes expressed.

Change

These Poems are about Change:

Nothing's Changed (pages 4-5)
Blessing (pages 8-9)
What Were They Like? (pages 16-17)
Search For My Tongue (pages 18-19)

Love After Love (pages 24-25)
This Room (pages 26-27)
Presents from my Aunts in Pakistan (pages 28-29)

Q1   Write a couple of sentences about a change that has happened in your life.

....

....

....

....

Q2   Choose a poem that you know from the top of the page.
Describe the change that happens in this poem.

....

....

....

....

....

EXAM-STYLE QUESTION   Q3   Compare the ways the poets describe change in 'This Room' and one other poem.

Compare:

   •   whether the change described is a good thing or a bad thing

   •   the poetic devices used to describe the change

   •   the feelings connected to the change.

EXAM-STYLE QUESTION   Q4   'What Were They Like?' discusses changes caused by war.
Compare 'What Were They Like' with another poem that discusses negative change.

Compare:

   •   the changes that take place

   •   how layout is used

   •   the feelings and attitudes in the poems.

People

These Poems are about specific People:

Island Man (pages 6-7)
Two Scavengers in a Truck... (pages 10-11)
Night of the Scorpion (pages 12-13)
Vultures (pages 14-15)

Search For My Tongue (pages 18-19)
Half-Caste (pages 22-23)
Presents from my Aunts in Pakistan (pages 28-29)
Not my Business (pages 30-31)
Hurricane Hits England (pages 32-33)

Q1   Write a paragraph about a person or group of people who are important to you.

....

....

....

....

Q2   Choose a character or group of characters from one of the poems at the top of the page.
How does this person / do these people mix with other people in the poem?

....

....

....

....

....

EXAM-STYLE QUESTION   Q3   'Hurricane Hits England' is about a person who feels homesick.
Compare the ways people are presented in 'Hurricane Hits England' and one other poem.

Compare:

• what the reader learns about the people in the poem

• the language devices used

• the feelings expressed in the poems.

EXAM-STYLE QUESTION   Q4   Compare the ways that people and their community are described in 'Two Scavengers
in a Truck, Two Beautiful People in a Mercedes' and one other poem.

Compare:

• whether the descriptions are positive or negative

• the poetic devices used to describe them

• the poets' attitudes towards society.

First Person

These Poems use the First Person:

Nothing's Changed (pages 4-5)
Night of the Scorpion (pages 12-13)
Search For My Tongue (pages 18-19)
Half-Caste (pages 22-23)

This Room (pages 26-27)
Presents from my Aunts in Pakistan (pages 28-29)
Not my Business (pages 30-31)
Hurricane Hits England (pages 32-33)

Q1 Describe two reasons why you think a poet might decide to write in the first person.

i) ....

....

ii) ....

....

Q2 Yep, it's time for another of these questions — choose a poem that you know from the top of the page. How does using the first person make the poem's message more effective?

....

....

....

....

....

EXAM-STYLE QUESTION Q3 The use of the first person in 'Search For My Tongue' helps us understand the poet's thoughts and feelings. Compare how the first person is used in 'Search For My Tongue' and one other poem.

Compare:

- what the poems are about
- the feelings expressed
- the poets' reasons for writing in the first person.

EXAM-STYLE QUESTION Q4 The voice we hear in 'Nothing's Changed' is very angry. Compare this poem with one other poem that uses the first person to convey the feelings and attitudes of the poet.

Compare:

- what the poets are trying to say
- how the first person is used
- the feelings and attitudes in the poems
- your opinion of the ideas in the poems.

Specific Cultural References

These Poems have Specific Cultural References:

Limbo (pages 2-3)
Nothing's Changed (pages 4-5)
Two Scavengers in a Truck... (pages 10-11)
Night of the Scorpion (pages 12-13)
What Were They Like? (pages 16-17)

Search For My Tongue (pages 18-19)
Presents from my Aunts in Pakistan (pages 28-29)
Not my Business (pages 30-31)
Hurricane Hits England (pages 32-33)

Q1   Describe a culture that you feel part of, or that you have experienced.

....

....

....

....

Q2   See those poems in the box at the top? Pick one.
In this poem, which culture does the poet describe, and what impression do we get of this culture?

....

....

....

....

....

EXAM-STYLE QUESTION

Q3   'Two Scavengers in a Truck, Two Beautiful People in a Mercedes' describes the
gap between the rich and poor of San Francisco. Choose another poem that uses
specific cultural references and compare it with 'Two Scavengers...'

Compare:

- the cultural details that are described

- the attitudes of the poets

- the poets' reasons for using specific cultural references.

EXAM-STYLE QUESTION

Q4   Compare the use of specific cultural references in 'Hurricane Hits England'
and one other poem.

Compare:

- the different cultural details that are described

- the language devices used

- the poets' feelings about the cultures they describe.

Description

Q1   Think about the funniest thing you've ever seen. Describe it in a brilliant and poetic way.

....

....

....

....

Q2   Pick a poem. A real beauty. One you know well. One from the box at the top of the page.
      How effective do you think the poet's descriptions are?

....

....

....

....

....

EXAM-STYLE   Q3   Compare the ways the poets describe particular places in 'Nothing's Changed' and one
QUESTION   other poem.

      Compare:

      •   the poets' attitudes towards the places described

      •   the use of poetic devices to create a particular impression of a place

      •   whether the place described is unique.

EXAM-STYLE   Q4   Traditional Pakistani clothes are described in 'Presents from my Aunts in Pakistan'.
QUESTION   Compare 'Presents...' with one other poem that uses interesting descriptions.

      Compare:

      •   how the poet uses poetic devices to create a particular impression

      •   the poets' feelings towards who/what is being described

      •   whether the descriptions are important to the poem's overall impact or not, and why.

Metaphor

These Poems use Metaphors:

Blessing (pages 8-9)

Vultures (pages 14-15)

Search For My Tongue (pages 18-19)

Half-Caste (pages 22-23)

This Room (pages 26-27)

> Metaphors are a way of describing things by saying that they are something else e.g. "my car is a heap of old rubbish".

Q1   Write down metaphors from two of the poems in the list above.

i)   ....

      ....

ii)   ....

      ....

Q2   Sorry if this is getting a bit repetitive but I'm afraid that's just the way it is.
      Select a poem from that box up there and explain why the poet's use of metaphors is effective.

      ....

      ....

      ....

      ....

      ....

EXAM-STYLE QUESTION   Q3   Compare the use of metaphors in 'This Room' and one other poem.

Compare:

- the types of metaphor used

- what feelings and attitudes are expressed by the metaphors

- how important you think the metaphors are to the overall impact of the poems.

EXAM-STYLE QUESTION   Q4   Compare the use of metaphors in 'Vultures' and one other poem.

Compare:

- what the poems are about

- the different uses and effects of metaphors

- how effective you think the metaphors are.

Unusual Presentation

These Poems have Unusual Presentation:

Limbo (pages 2-3)
Nothing's Changed (pages 4-5)
Island Man (pages 6-7)
Two Scavengers in a Truck... (pages 10-11)

What Were They Like? (pages 16-17)
Search For My Tongue (pages 18-19)
Unrelated Incidents (pages 20-21)
Presents from my Aunts in Pakistan (pages 28-29)

Q1   Why do you think a poet might decide to use an unusual style of presentation?

....

....

....

....

Q2   Explain what effect the style of presentation has in one of
the poems that you are familiar with from the box above.

....

....

....

....

....

EXAM-STYLE QUESTION

Q3   Compare 'What Were They Like?' with one other poem that has unusual presentation.

Compare:

- the effect the poets are trying to create by using this style of presentation

- the feelings and attitudes expressed in the poem

- how important you think the style of presentation is to the poems' message.

EXAM-STYLE QUESTION

Q4   'Unrelated Incidents' has a very unusual shape on the page.
Compare this with one other poem that uses unusual presentation.

Compare:

- what the poems are about

- the feelings or ideas expressed in the poems

- how they use unusual presentation to express these feelings or ideas

- your opinion of each poem.

Non-Standard English

These Poems use Non-Standard English:

Limbo (pages 2-3)   Unrelated Incidents (pages 20-21)
Island Man (pages 6-7)   Half-Caste (pages 22-23)

Q1   What is "non-standard English"?

....

....

....

....

Q2   I imagine you've got the gist by now... choose a poem that you know from the top of the page.
Why do you think the poet has chosen to write in non-standard English in this poem?

....

....

....

....

....

EXAM-STYLE QUESTION   **Q3**   Non-standard English is used in some poems to show the cultural background of the poets.
Compare the use of non-standard English in 'Limbo' and one other poem.

Compare:

- the cultural backgrounds

- the feelings expressed in the poems

- how and why non-standard English is used to express these feelings.

EXAM-STYLE QUESTION   **Q4**   Compare the use of non-standard English in 'Unrelated Incidents' and one other poem.

Compare:

- the feelings or ideas expressed in the poems

- how and why non-standard English is used

- how effective you think the use of non-standard English is in the two poems.

Particular Places

These Poems are about Particular Places:

Nothing's Changed (pages 4-5)
Island Man (pages 6-7)
Two Scavengers in a Truck... (pages 10-11)
Vultures (pages 14-15)

What Were They Like? (16-17)
Presents from my Aunts in Pakistan (pages 28-29)
Hurricane Hits England (pages 32-33)

Q1   Write a couple of sentences to describe your favourite place.

....

....

....

....

Q2   Right, it's time to choose another poem from the blue box of destiny at the top of the page.
      What kind of image do you get of the place described in the poem?

....

....

....

....

....

EXAM-STYLE QUESTION Q3   Compare 'Nothing's Changed' with one other poem in which the poet describes
      a place that is important to them.

      Compare:

      •   why these places are important to the poets

      •   what impression the poets give of these places

      •   how they use poetic devices to create this impression.

EXAM-STYLE QUESTION Q4   Compare how particular places are shown to be important in 'Hurricane
      Hits England' and one other poem.

      Compare:

      •   how the poets describe the places

      •   the ideas and attitudes expressed in the poems

      •   how the poems make you feel about the places they describe.

Two Cultures

These Poems are about Two Cultures:

Island Man (pages 6-7)
Search For My Tongue (pages 18-19)
Unrelated Incidents (pages 20-21)

Half-Caste (pages 22-23)
Presents from my Aunts in Pakistan (pages 28-29)
Hurricane Hits England (pages 32-33)

Q1   Do you feel that you belong to just one culture, or to more than one? Explain your answer.

....

....

....

....

Q2   Like you've done on every single page of this section, pick a poem that you've studied from
the list above. Does the poet think that the two cultures can mix well or not? Explain your answer.

....

....

....

....

....

EXAM-STYLE QUESTION   Q3   Compare the effect of contrasting cultures in 'Island Man' and one other poem.

Compare:

- whether the different cultures clash or mix together

- the poetic devices used to show the contrast

- the feelings and attitudes shown by the contrast.

EXAM-STYLE QUESTION   Q4   Compare 'Presents from my Aunts in Pakistan' to another poem
that involves a conflict of two cultures.

Compare:

- the ways the different cultures are described

- how the poets present the conflict between cultures

- the poets' feelings about belonging to two cultures.

Universal Ideas

These Poems are about Universal Ideas:

Nothing's Changed (pages 4-5)
Two Scavengers in a Truck... (pages 10-11)
Vultures (pages 14-15)
Half-Caste (pages 22-23)

Love After Love (pages 24-25)
This Room (pages 26-27)
Hurricane Hits England (pages 32-33)

Q1 Describe a film, TV programme, play or book that you have seen or read that made you think about a particular issue.

....

....

....

....

Q2 Pick a number from 1 to 7. Congratulations, you've just chosen a poem from the box at the top. What is the universal idea in this poem? How does the poet present this idea?

....

....

....

....

....

EXAM-STYLE QUESTION **Q3** 'Vultures' deals with the theme of good and evil in humans.
Compare 'Vultures' to one other poem that deals with a universal idea.

Compare:

- the introduction and presentation of ideas
- the attitudes expressed by the poets
- the poets' conclusions.

EXAM-STYLE QUESTION **Q4** Compare the universal ideas in 'Hurricane Hits England' and one other poem.

Compare:

- the ways the poets discuss these ideas in their poems
- the opinions the poets present about these ideas
- how the poets relate these ideas to more specific themes in the poem.

Traditions

These Poems are about Traditions:

Limbo (pages 2-3)
Night of the Scorpion (pages 12-13)
What Were They Like? (pages 16-17)

Presents from my Aunts in Pakistan (pages 28-29)
Hurricane Hits England (pages 32-33)

Q1 Describe a tradition that you take part in.

....

....

....

....

Q2 OK, I promise this is the last time. Pick a poem from the box and explain what impression the poet gives of the traditions it describes.

....

....

....

....

....

EXAM-STYLE QUESTION **Q3** Compare 'Presents from my Aunts in Pakistan' with one other poem that describes cultural traditions.

Compare:

- the different traditions described

- the poetic devices used to describe the traditions

- whether the poets present these traditions as a good thing or a bad thing.

EXAM-STYLE QUESTION **Q4** Compare the ways traditions are presented in 'Night of the Scorpion' and one other poem.

Compare:

- the language used to describe the traditions

- whether the poet feels a part of these traditions or an outsider to them

- your responses to the traditions described.

<u>Acknowledgements</u>

The Publisher would like to thank:

<u>Chinua Achebe</u> 'Vultures' from Collected Poems published by Carcanet reprinted by permission of David Higham Associates.

<u>Tatamkhulu Afrika</u> 'Nothing's Changed' by Tatamkhulu Afrika from Night Rider: Selected Poems, published by Kwela Books

<u>John Agard</u> 'Half Caste' copyright © 1996 by John Agard reproduced by kind permission of John Agard c/o Caroline Sheldon Literary Agency Ltd.

<u>Moniza Alvi</u> *Carrying My Wife*, Bloodaxe Books, 2000

<u>Sujata Bhatt</u> 'Search For My Tongue' from *Brunizem* (1998), reprinted by permission of the publishers, Carcanet Press Ltd.

<u>Edward Kamau Brathwaite</u> 'Limbo' from *The Arrivants: A New World Trilogy* (OUP, 1973), reprinted by permission of Oxford University Press.

<u>Imtiaz Dharker</u> *Postcards from god*, Bloodaxe Books, 1997; *I Speak for the Devil*, Bloodaxe Books 2001

<u>Nissim Ezekiel</u> 'Night of the Scorpion' from *Poverty Poems*, reproduced by permission of Oxford University Press India, New Delhi

<u>Lawrence Ferlinghetti</u> 'Two Scavengers in A Truck, Two Beautiful People In A Mercedes' By Lawrence Ferlinghetti, from THESE ARE MY RIVERS, copyright © 1979 by Lawrence Ferlinghetti. Reprinted by permission of New Directions Publishing Corp.

<u>Tom Leonard</u> 'Unrelated Incidents' © Tom Leonard, from *Intimate Voices* Etruscan Books, Devon

<u>Denise Levertov</u> 'What Were They Like?' from Selected Poems (Bloodaxe Books, 1986). Reproduced by permission of Pollinger Limited and the proprietor.

<u>Grace Nichols</u> 'Hurricane Hits England' copyright © Grace Nichols 1996 reproduced with permission of Curtis Brown Group Ltd & 'Island Man' copyright © Grace Nichols 1984 reproduced with permission of Curtis Brown Group Ltd.

<u>Niyi Osundare</u> 'Not My Business' from Songs of the Seasons (Heinemann Educational Books, Nigeria, 1990)

<u>Derek Walcott</u> 'Love After Love' from SEA GRAPES by Derek Walcott. Copyright © 1976 by Derek Walcott. Reprinted by permission of Farrar, Straus and Giroux, LLC

<u>Photographs:</u>

'Children' With thanks to the District 6 Museum
'Traffic' With thanks to Ian Britton of Freefoto.com

Every effort has been made to locate copyright holders and obtain permission to reproduce poems and photographs. For those poems and photographs where it has been difficult to trace the copyright holder of the work, we would be grateful for information. If any copyright holder would like us to make an amendment to the acknowledgements, please notify us and we will gladly update the book at the next reprint. Thank you.